CREATIVE COLORING

DECORATIVE TYPE

METRO BOOKS
New York

METRO BOOKS
New York

An Imprint of Sterling Publishing Co., Inc.
1166 Avenue of the Americas
New York, NY 10036

ISBN 978-1-4351-6308-9

For information about custom editions, special sales, and premium and corporate purchases,
please contact Sterling Special Sales at 800-805-5489 or specialsales@sterlingpublishing.com.

Manufactured in China

2 4 6 8 10 9 7 5 3 1

www.sterlingpublishing.com

Cover by Ana Bjezancevic

Illustrations by Sam Loman, Jake McDonald, Steve Turner, Suzanne Washington,
Felicity French and Simon Ålander

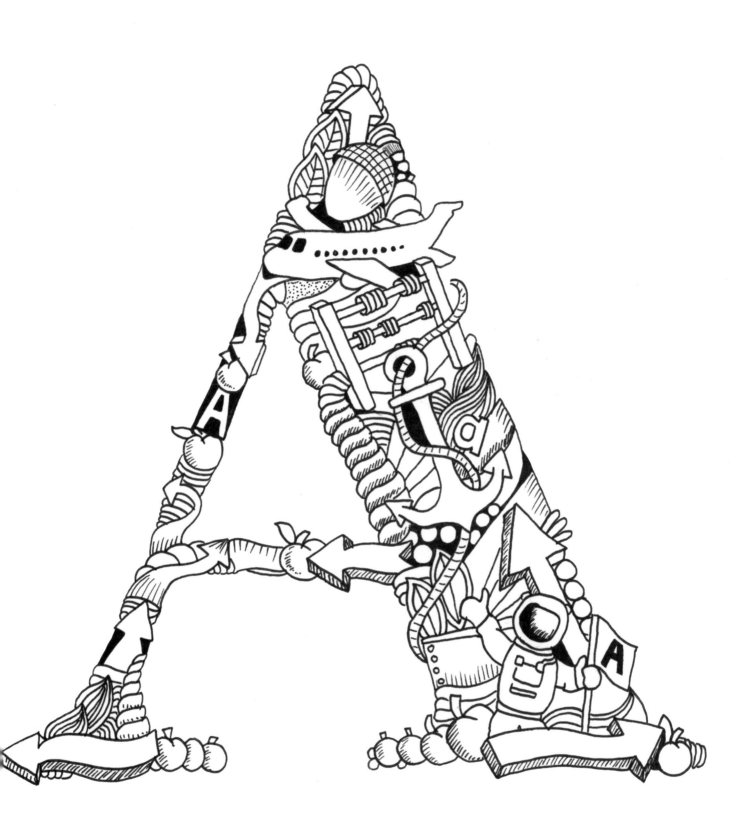

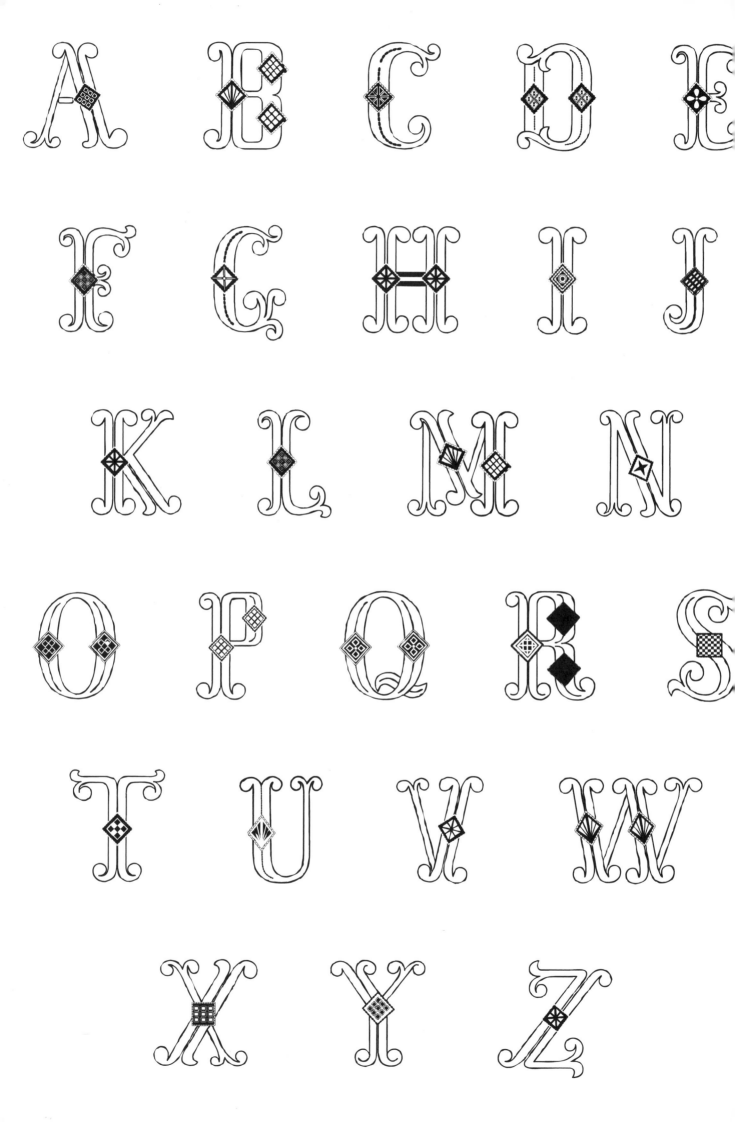

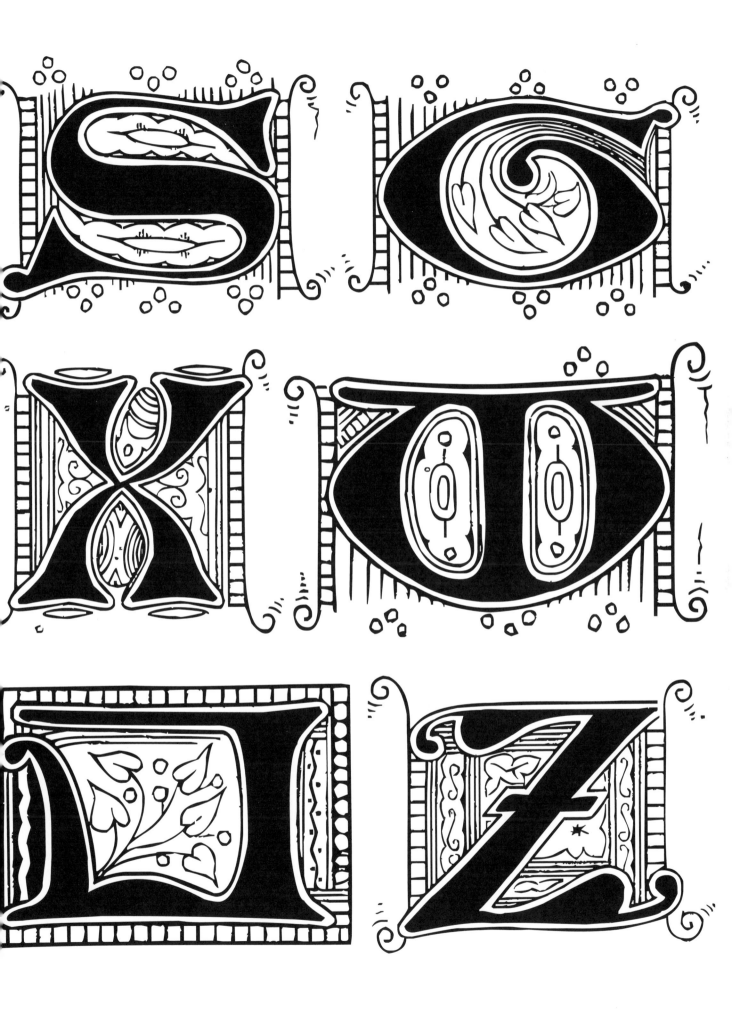

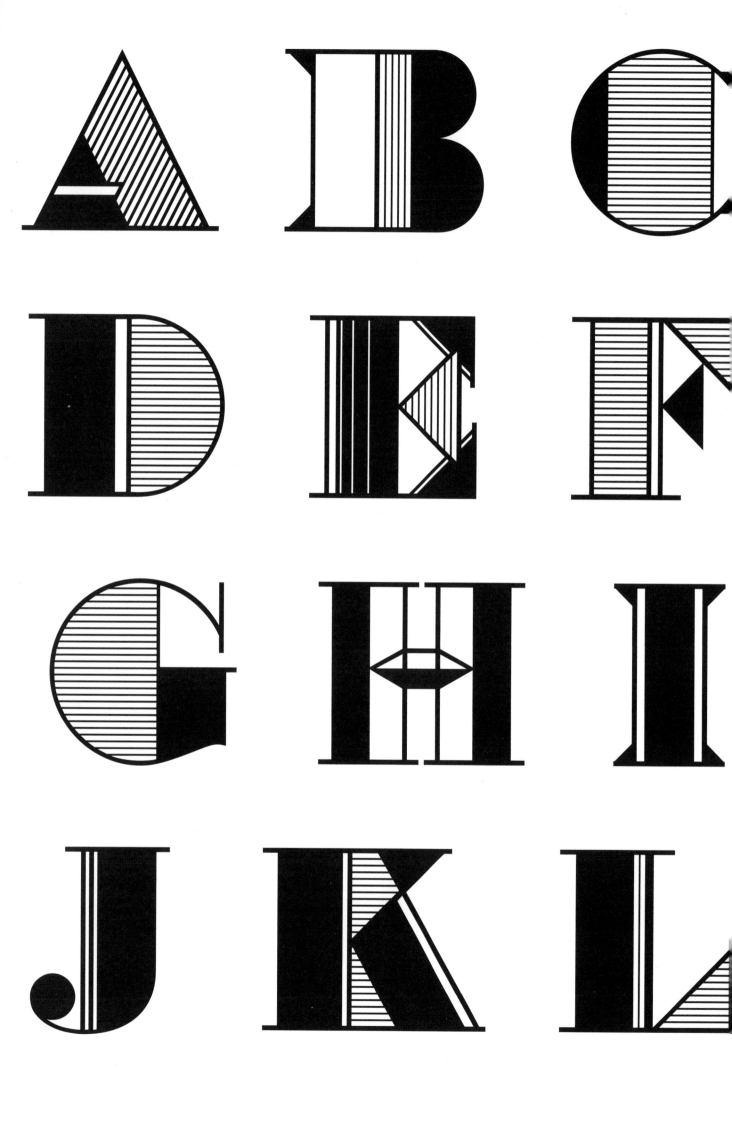

A B C

D E F G

H I J K

L M N

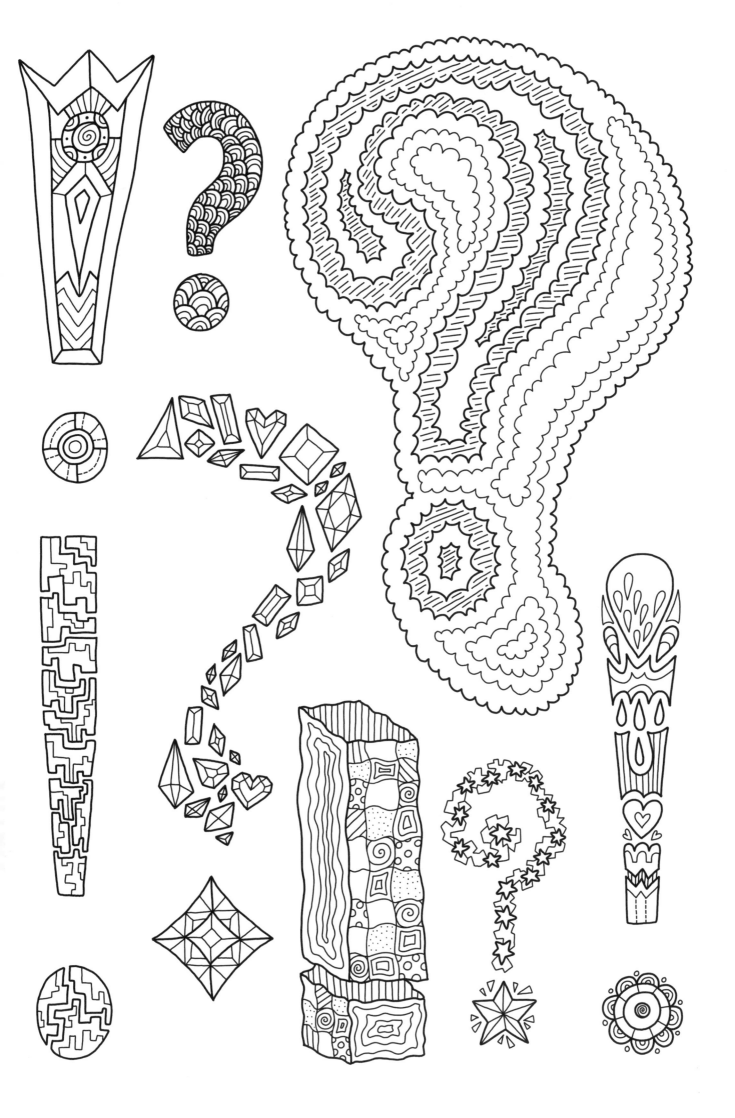

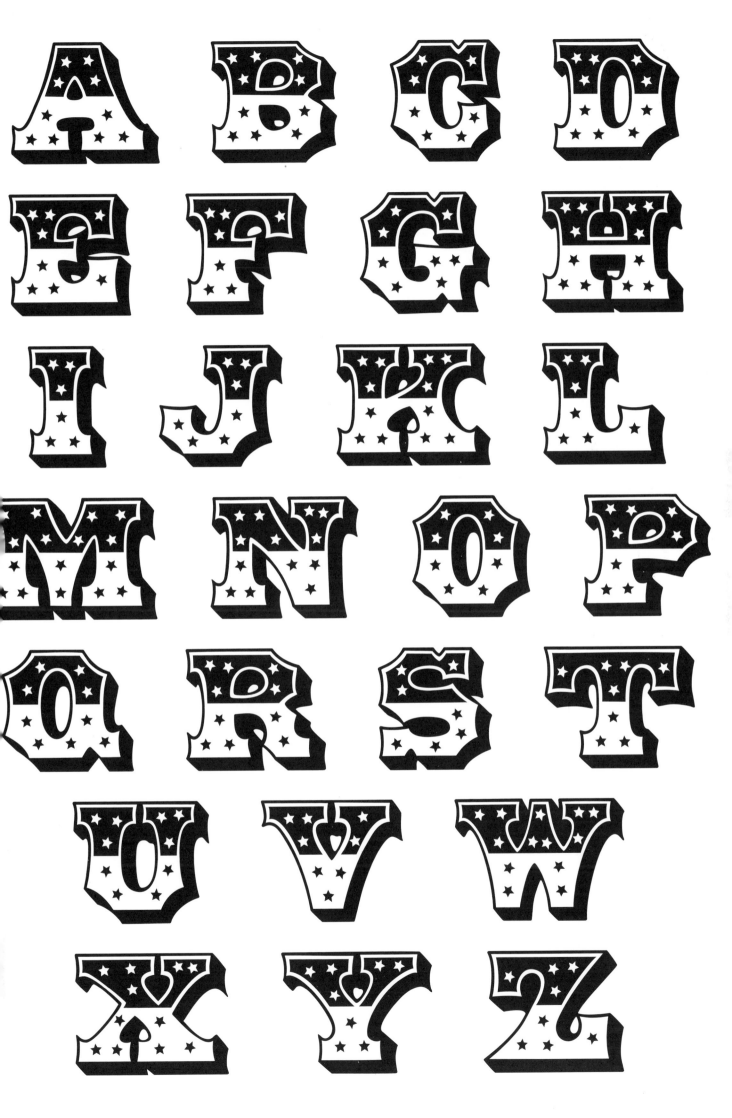

F G H i H i H K L
O n V j J M
P R T U B
P R S
O q X A
Y q W i V

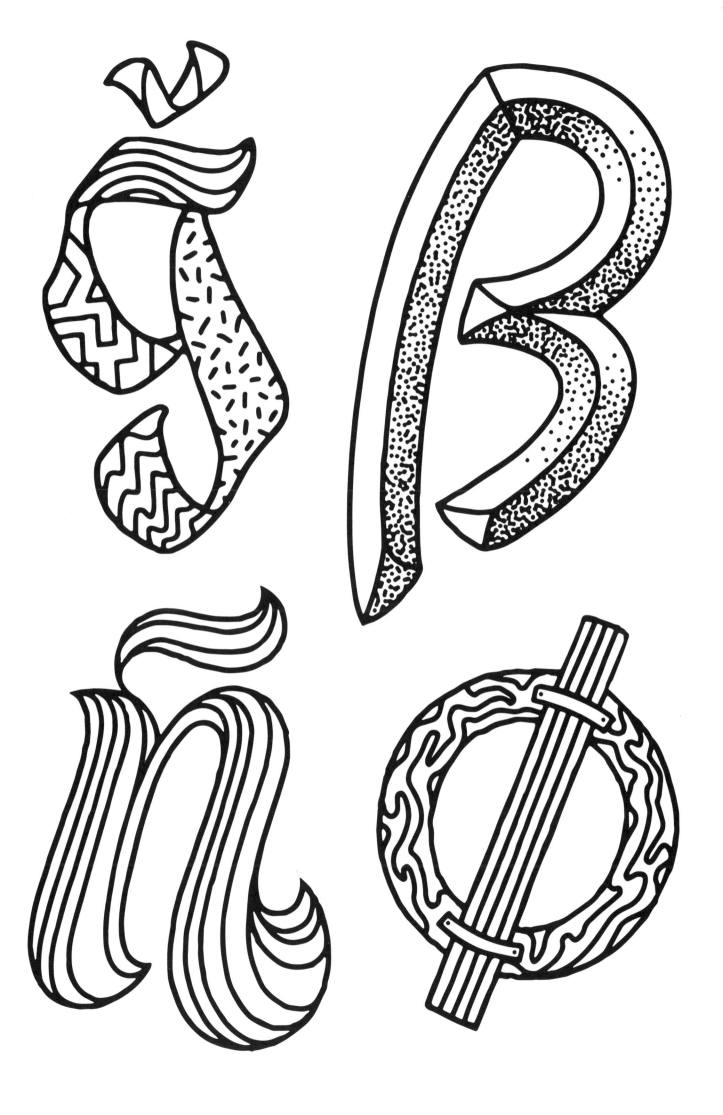

A B C D E
F G H I J
K L M N
O P Q R
S T U V
W X Y Z

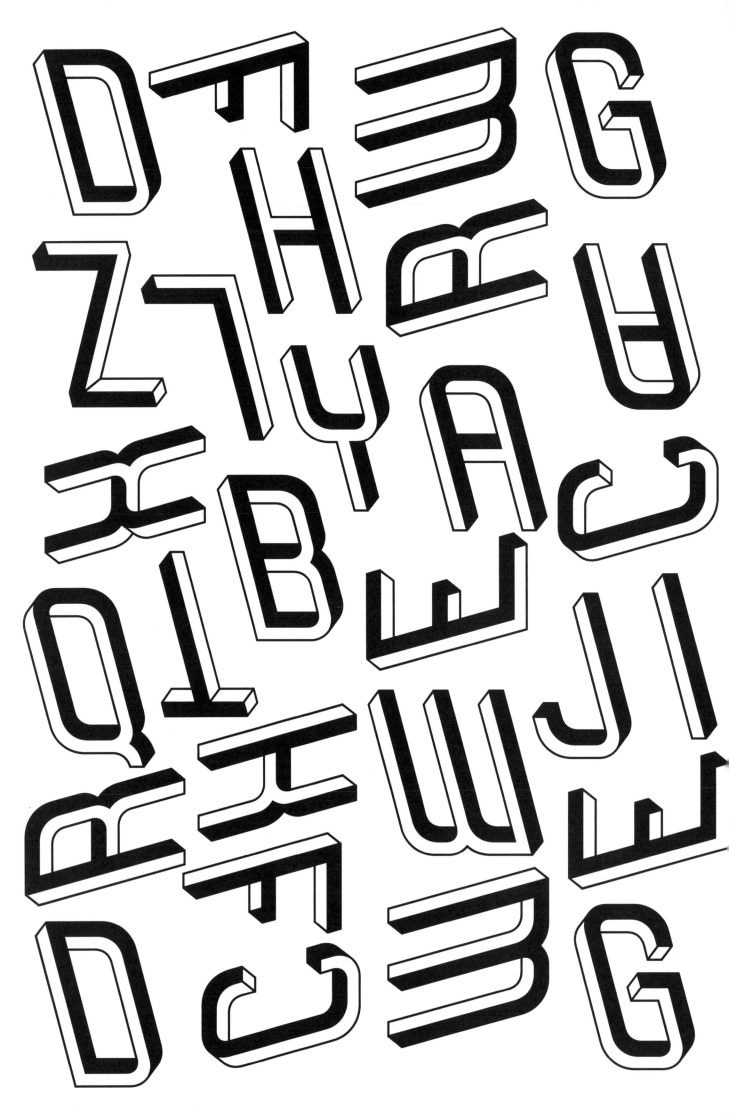

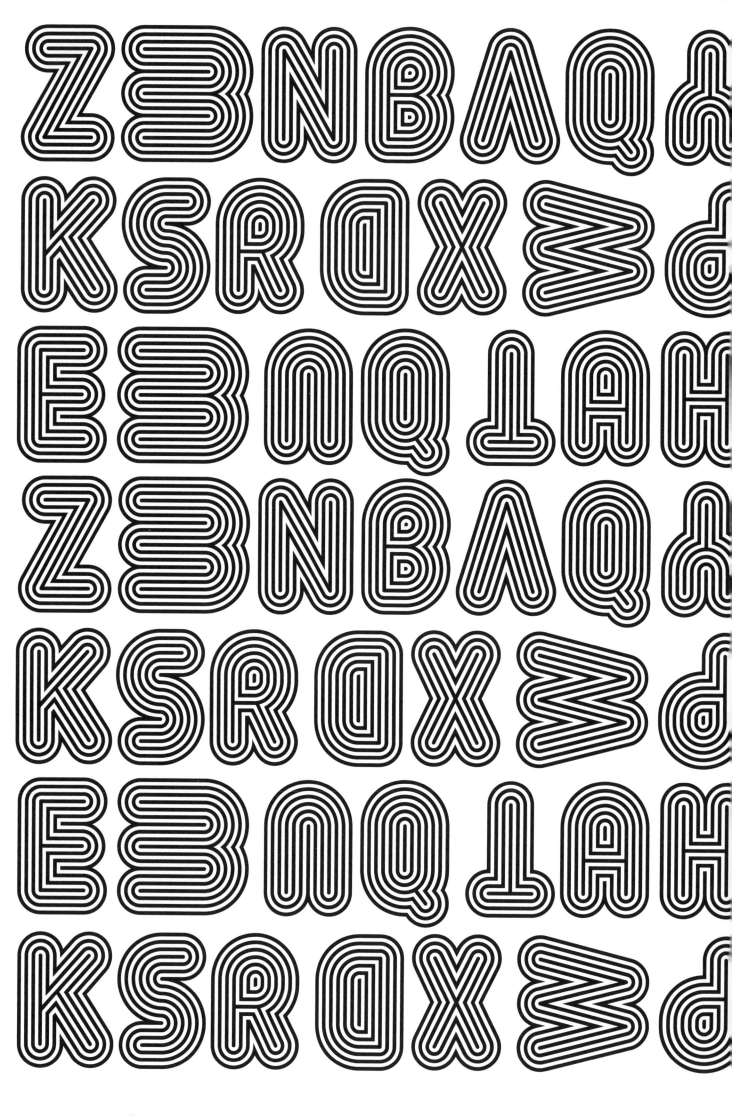

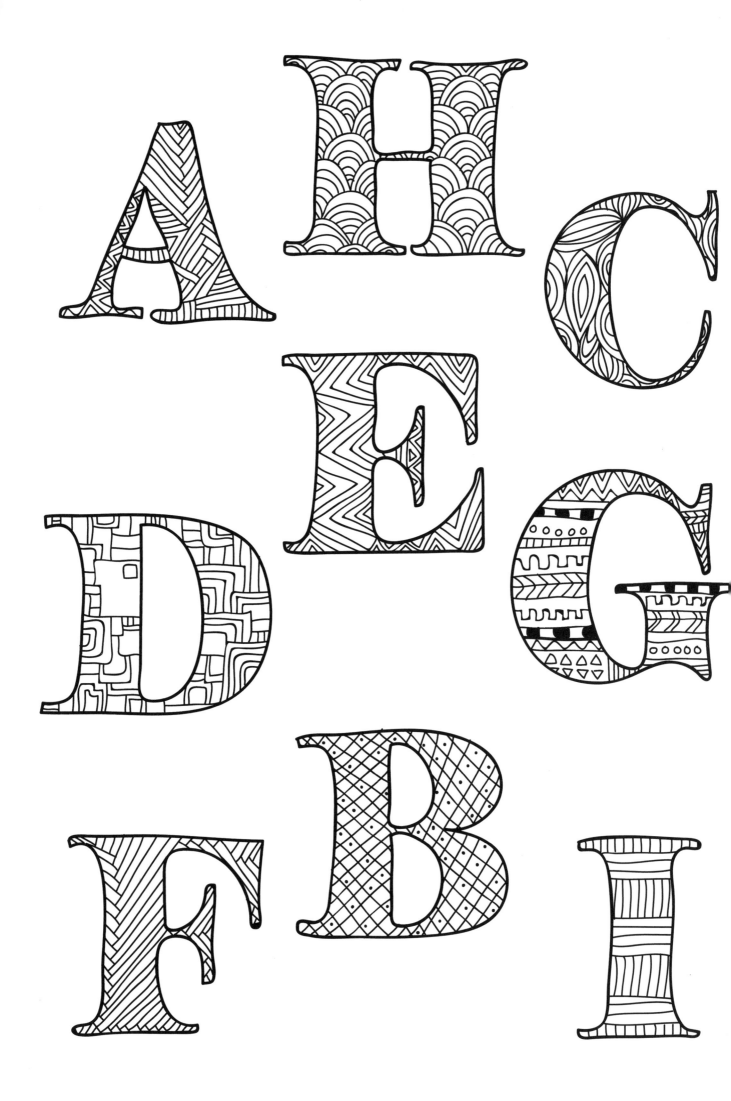

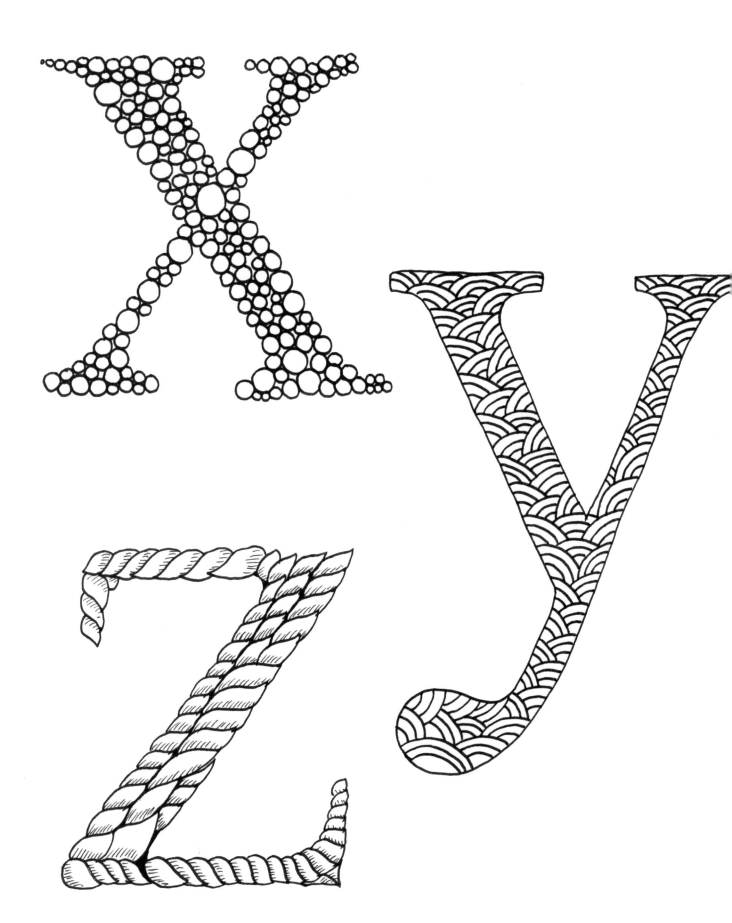

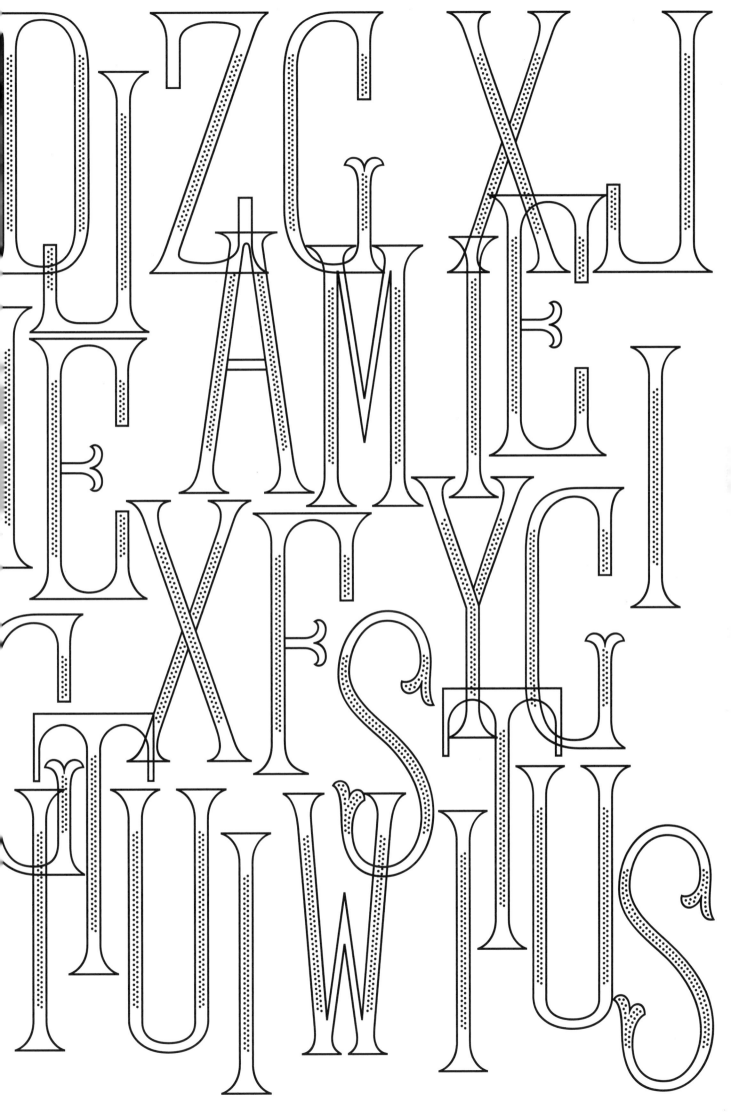

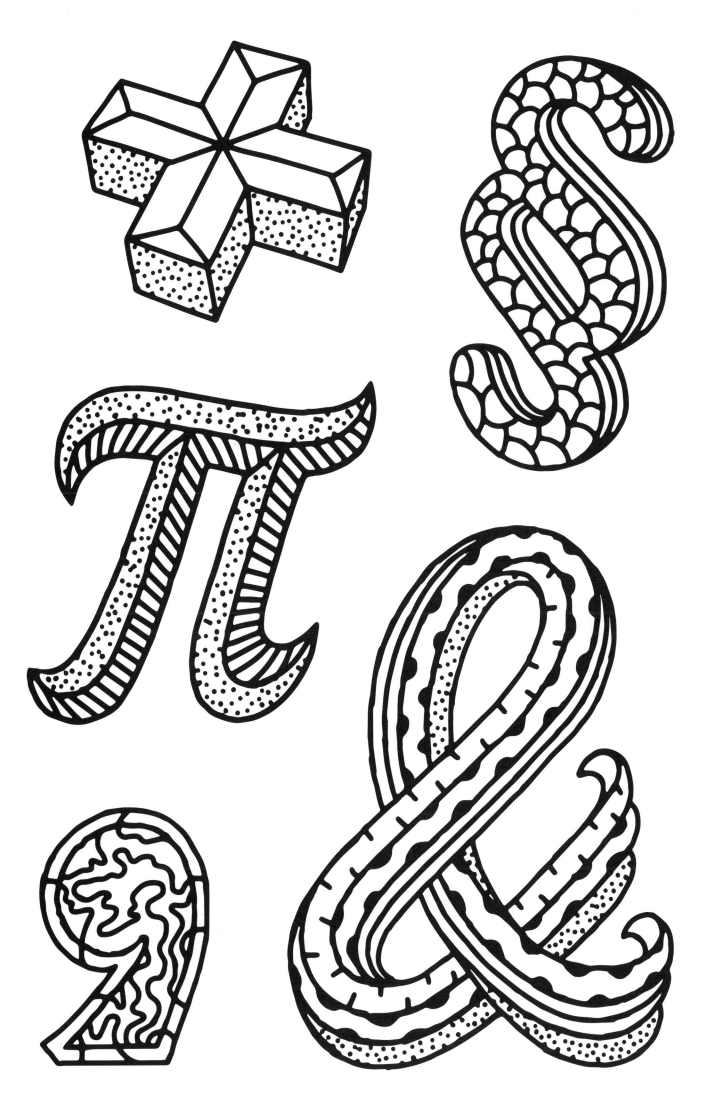

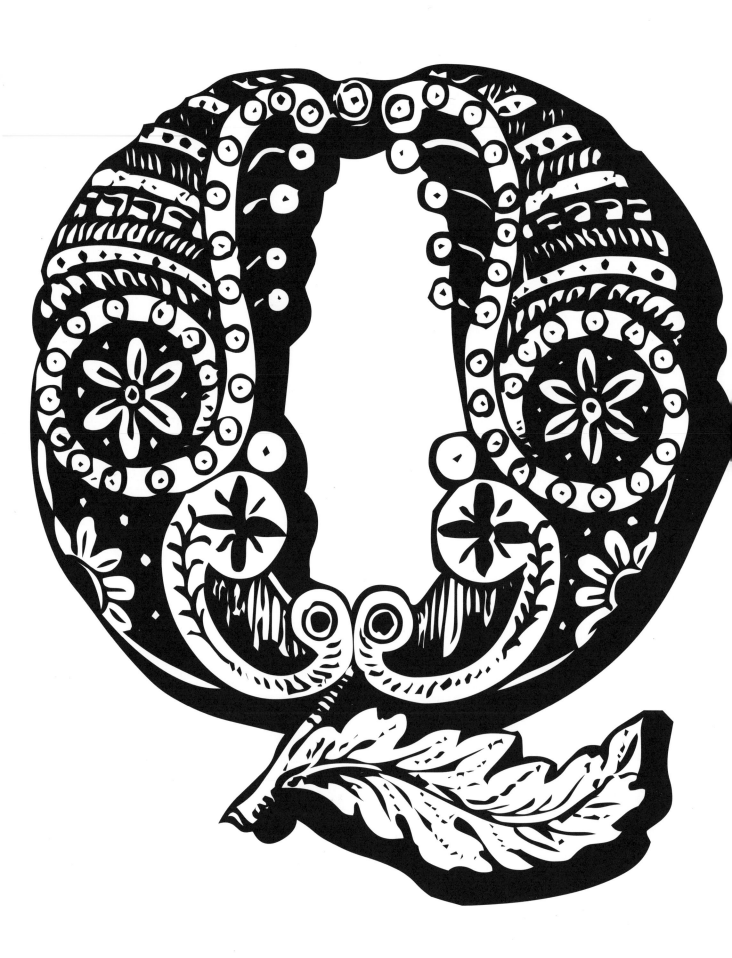

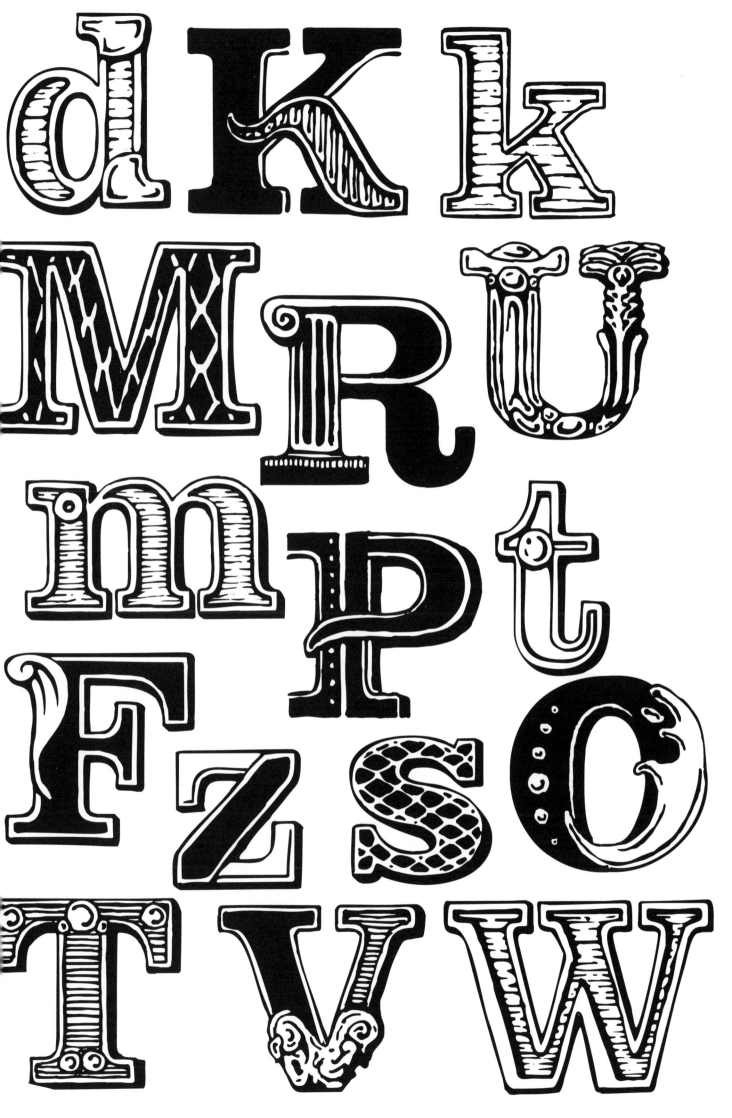

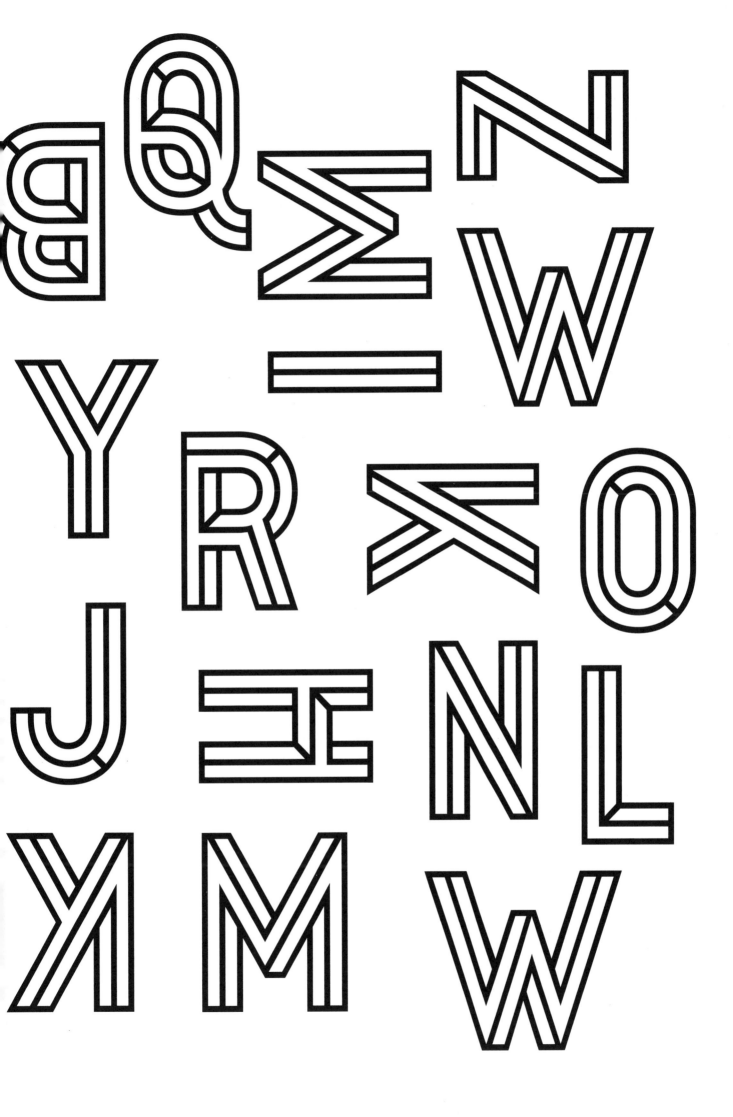

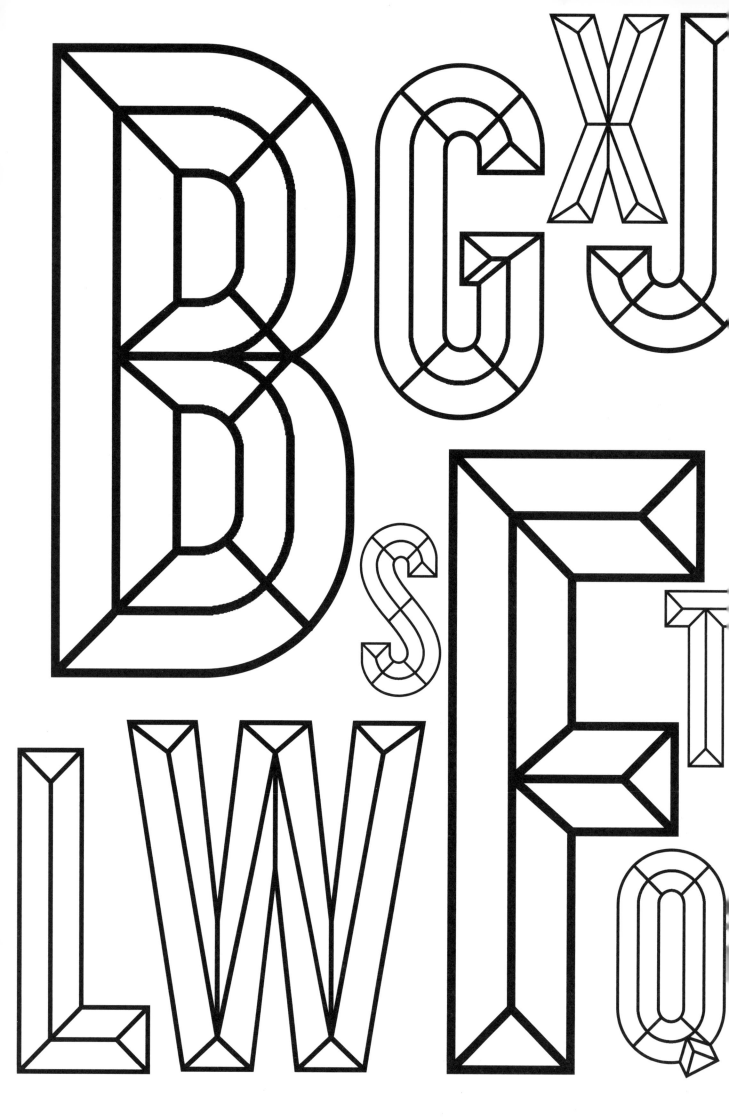

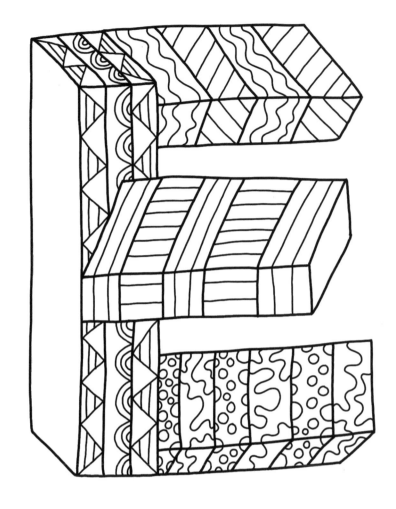

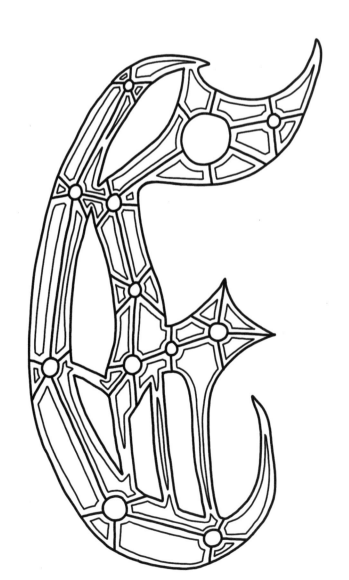

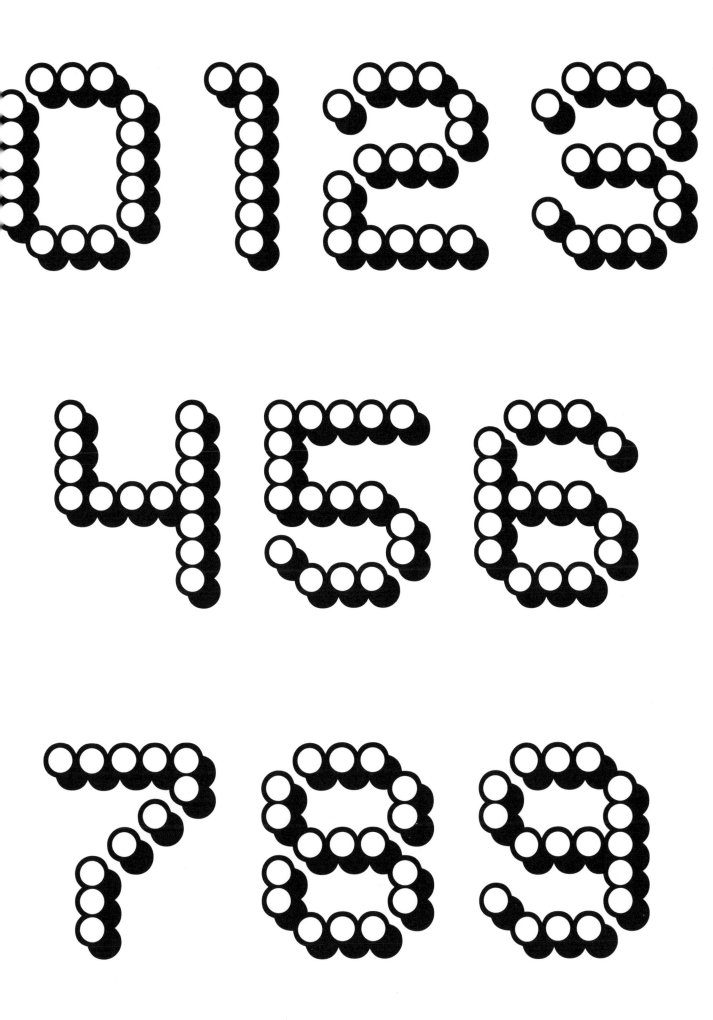

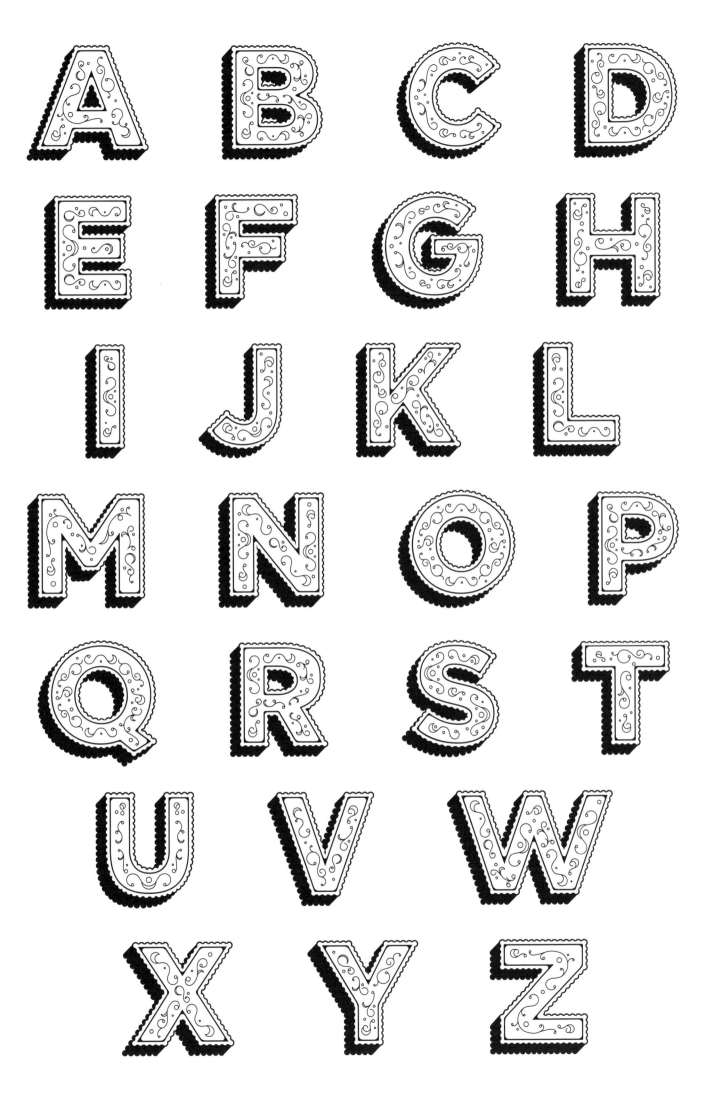

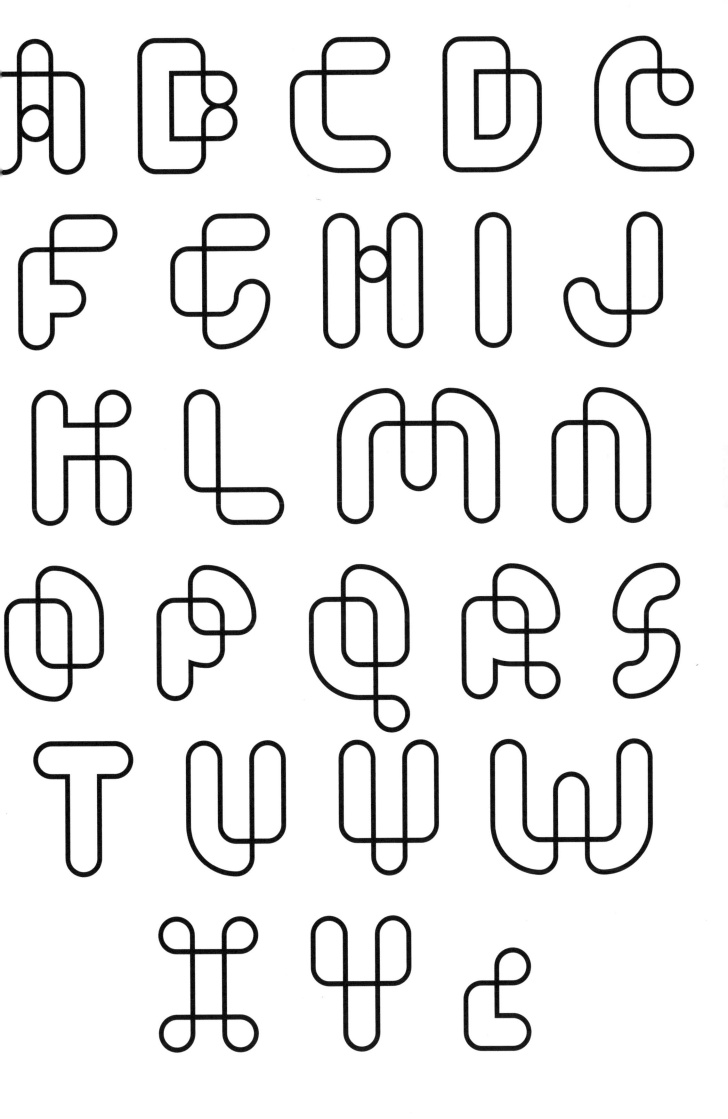

ABCDEFG
HIJKLM
NOPQRS
TUVW
XYZ

A B C

D E F G

H I J K

L M N

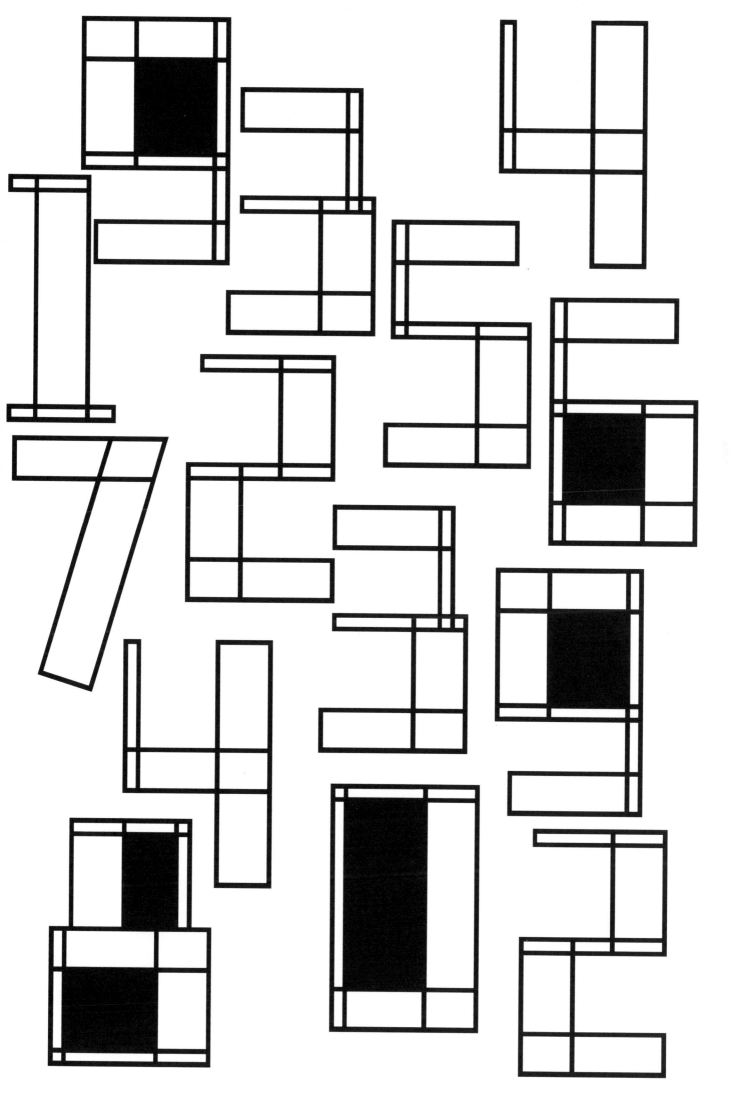

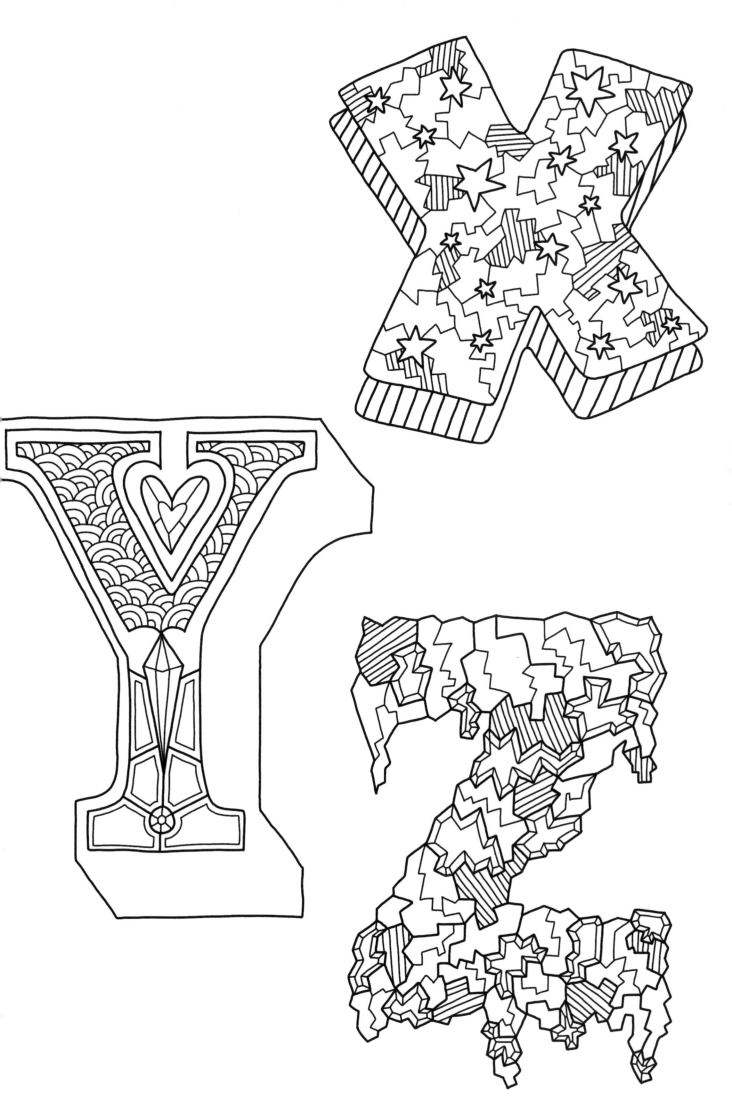

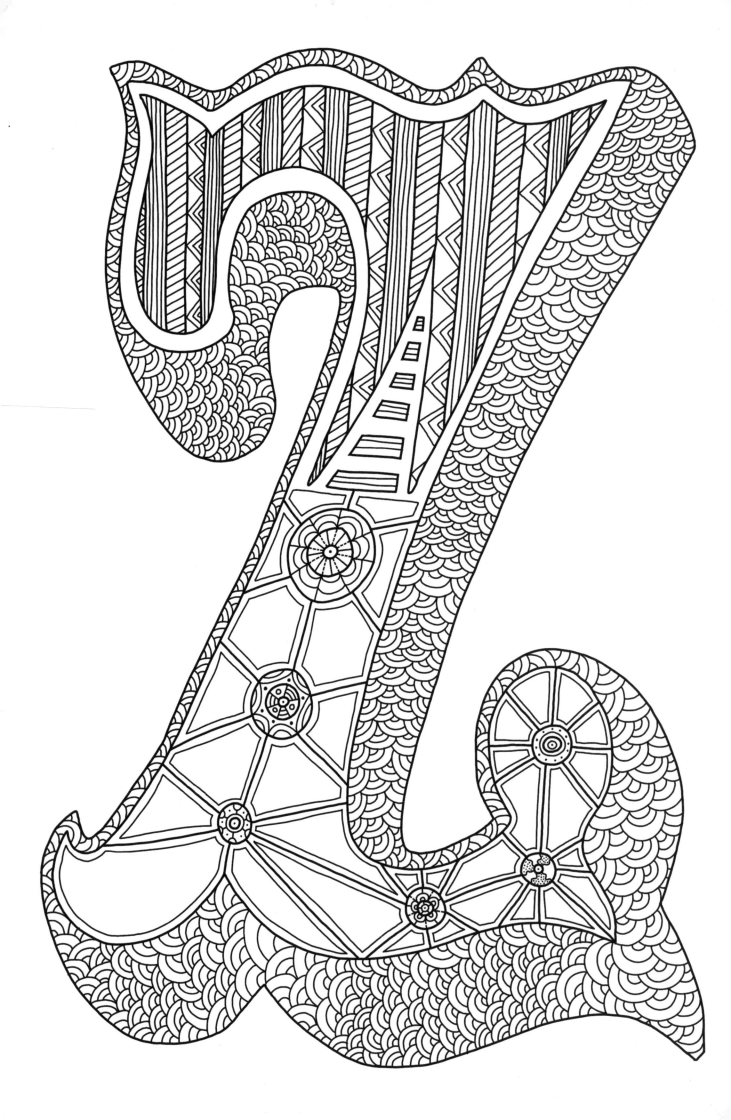